W9-AKV-286

The Magic School Bus Falls with the Leaves

by Quinlan B. Lee

SCHOLASTIC INC.

New York   Toronto   London   Auckland   Sydney
Mexico City   New Delhi   Hong Kong   Buenos Aires

"Do you see this leaf?"
asks D.A.
"It is green.
But this leaf is yellow.
Why?"

"Wait and see,"
says Ms. Frizzle.
"Let's go visit a tree."

"Take a seat.
Let's go see the trees!"
says Ms. Frizzle.
"Now I feel green,"
says Arnold.

"Now grab a leaf," Ms. Frizzle says. "I miss my seat," says Arnold.

Each leaf is green with yellow or red underneath.
When the leaf loses the green, you can see the other colors.

When the leaf loses the green, it is time to fall off the tree!
"I feel sick again!" Arnold says.

"See, Arnold, leaves make fall fun," says Ms. Frizzle. "You will see green leaves again in spring!"

"Now we're leaving the leaves," says Ms. Frizzle.